Guitar Grade 1

Pieces & Exercises
for Trinity Guildhall examinations

2010-2015

Published by:
Trinity College London
89 Albert Embankment
London SE1 7TP UK

T +44 (0)20 7820 6100
F +44 (0)20 7820 6161
E music@trinityguildhall.co.uk
www.trinityguildhall.co.uk

Music processed by Artemis Music Ltd.
Printed in England by Halstan & Co. Ltd, Amersham, Bucks.

Vals

Ferdinando Carulli
(1770-1841)

In the Hall of the Mountain King

from *Peer Gynt Suite* no. 1 op. 46

arr. Rebecca Baulch

Edvard Grieg
(1843-1907)

Practice with metronome at 80 or less

El conde olinos

A Spanish folk song

arr. Eythor Thorlaksson

Juan Hidalgo Montoya

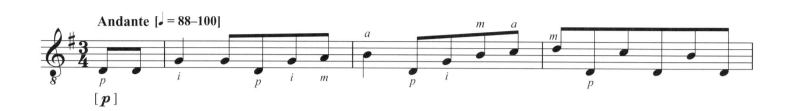

Practice with metronome at 80 or less

Marrakech

Claude Gagnon

The Moon's a Balloon

Lee Sollory
(born 1959)

Day of the Match

Gary Ryan
(born 1969)

Habanera Era

Gary Ryan
(born 1969)

Olinda

Frevo

Jonathan Preiss
(born 1971)

Olé José

Debbie Cracknell

Technical Suite (Exercises)

Candidates choosing Option ii) Technical Suite in the Technical Work section of the examination must prepare the following exercises.

1. Step by Step (scales)

To be prepared *apoyando* or *tirando* at candidate's choice.*

2. Thumb Thing in the Air (thumb articulation and chromatic scales)

To be prepared *apoyando* or *tirando* at candidate's choice. Played with RH thumb.

* *apoyando* = rest stroke; *tirando* = free stroke.

3. Farewell (arpeggios)

4. Right Hand Exercises

a)

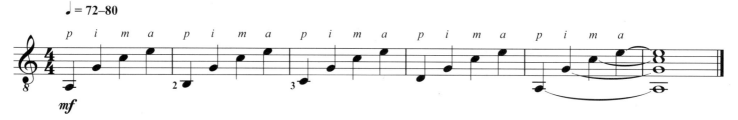

b)

Table of Key Signatures

Sharp Key Signatures (Major)

Sharp Key Signatures (Minor)

Flat Key Signatures (Major)

Flat Key Signatures (Minor)

Table of Key Signatures

Sharp Key Signatures (Major)

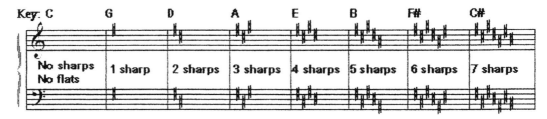

Sharp Key Signatures (Minor)

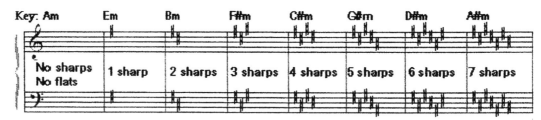

Flat Key Signatures (Major)

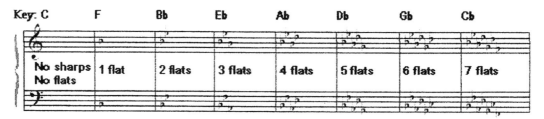

Flat Key Signatures (Minor)

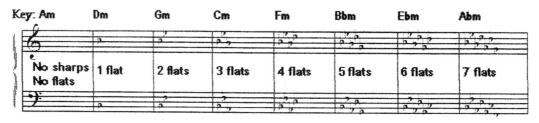